# Moses in the Bulrushes

Long ago in Egypt there lived a group of people called the Israelites.

They lived **peacefully** among the Egyptian people, where some became rich.

After many years, there were a lot of Israelite people living in Egypt.

The king of Egypt, or Pharaoh, wasn't happy that there were so many Israelites in his country.

He thought that one day they would try to **take over Egypt**.

Pharaoh forced the Israelites to become slaves. They had to work for the Egyptian people to build new towns, and were treated harshly.

But the number of Israelite people **continued to grow.**

Pharaoh needed another plan to stop the Israelites becoming powerful.

Pharaoh ordered that all Israelite baby boys were killed, but that girls were allowed to live.

Egyptian soldiers were sent to carry out the awful task. They marched into Israelite towns.

One Israelite family had a **tiny baby boy.** They managed to hide him from the Pharaoh's soldiers.

Sshh!

For three months they were able to keep the baby boy a secret.

Waah!

But as he began to grow **bigger and noisier,** this became more difficult.

One day, the baby's mother came up with a plan. She made a **strong basket** and coated it with tar to make it waterproof.

The baby's sister, Miriam, watched closely.

Then they wrapped
the baby in a blanket
to keep him warm, and
put him in the basket.

Then Miriam and her mother crept down to the river and placed the basket with the sleeping baby among the **tall bulrushes.**

The little basket bobbed gently on the water.

Miriam's mother returned home to stop people becoming suspicious. Miriam hid in the bulrushes and kept watch over her baby brother.

After a while, Miriam saw some people approaching – it was Pharaoh's daughter and her servants!

The princess had come to the **river** to bathe.

Suddenly the princess noticed the little basket floating gently on the water.

"Quickly! Fetch that basket!" she ordered one of her servants.

The servant pulled the basket from the water and gasped when she saw the little baby boy inside. He began to cry.

"Give the child to me," said the princess, and she held him in her arms.

Suddenly, Miriam appeared before the princess. "Perhaps I could find someone to help look after the baby?"

"Yes," said the princess. "Find me a nurse."

Miriam hurried to bring her mother to the princess.

"I will pay you to look after this child, he will be brought up as my son and no harm will come to him."

Miriam and her mother were **overjoyed**.

The princess named the baby 'Moses', which means 'drawn out', just as he was drawn out of the water.

So as a small child, Moses stayed with his family, living **safely and happily** under the protection of the princess.

Then one day when he was old
enough, his mother and sister
took him to the Pharaoh's
palace to be with the princess.

"Thank you for looking after him," said the princess. So Moses was brought up as an Egyptian prince.

Little did he know that one day he would help to set the Israelite people free, under God's guidance.